Senses

Compiled by

Contents

Acknowledgements

The Editor and Publisher wish to thank the following who have kindly given permission for the use of copyright material:

Moira Andrew for 'I like' © 1996 Moira Andrew; Eric Finney for 'I can see you now' © 1996 Eric Finney; John Foster for 'The young fox' © 1996 John Foster; Richard James for 'Kitchen sounds' © 1996 Richard James; John Kitching for 'Grandad's beard' © 1996 John Kitching; Tony Mitton for 'Cookie sensations' © 1996 Tony Mitton; Judith Nicholls for 'Smelly story' © 1996 Judith Nicholls; Celia Warren for 'Sounds like magic' © 1996 Celia Warren.

I like

I like the taste of toothpaste,
tingling on my tongue.

I like the smell of sausages,
nuzzling at my nose.

I like the feel of sunshine
flickering on my face.

I like the sound of bells
echoing in my ears.

I like the sight of fairground lights
flashing in the dark.

Moira Andrew

Kitchen sounds

Porridge gloops
A sausage sizzles
The toaster clangs
The kettle whistles
Washing spins
People chatter
Knives chop
Dishes clatter
Taps gush
Pans clink
Water gurgles
In the sink.

The light clicks off
Night-time comes
And in the dark
The freezer hums.

Richard James

5

Cookie sensations

When I see a cookie in the baker's shop
my mouth starts to water and my eyes go pop.

When I hold the cookie in a paper bag
the crackle and the smell start to drive me mad.

But when I bite the cookie and begin to eat
the sound is crunchy and the taste is sweet.

Tony Mitton

Sounds like magic

I listened to a sea-shell
and thought I could hear
the rushing of the waves
inside my ear.

I held an empty egg-shell
close against my head
and thought I heard a pecking chick
hatching from its bed.

I found a hollow coconut
and listened for a sound
and thought I heard horses' hooves
pounding on the ground.

I took an empty teacup
to see what I might hear
and thought I heard a giant's voice
booming in my ear.

Celia Warren

Smelly story

I love . . .
the smell of bonfires
in November rain.

I hate . . .
the smell of smoky air
inside a crowded train.

I love . . .
the smell of apple pie
swimming in thick cream.

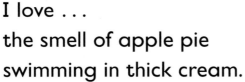

I hate . . .
the smell of soggy sprouts
or cabbage or sardine.

I love . . .
the smell of salty seas
or sand beneath my toes.

I hate . . .
the smell of sweaty socks
just underneath my nose.

Judith Nicholls

I can see you now

When I first met
My blind friend Grace
She said, 'Will you please let me
Touch your face?'

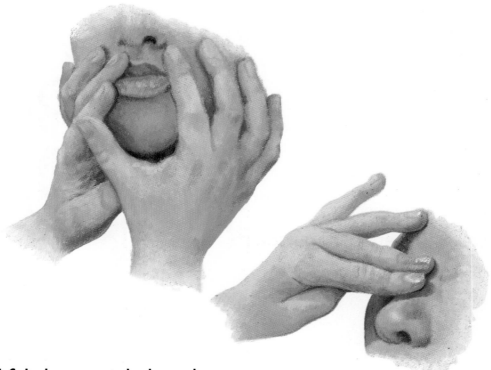

I felt her gentle hands
Upon my skin:
She felt my lips and eyebrows
Then my nose and cheeks and chin.

Last of all she felt my hair
And gently held my head.
Then with a lovely smile:
'I can see you now,' she said.

Eric Finney

The young fox

At night, the young fox pokes its head
Out of its den beneath the shed.

It listens with its pointed ears
To hear if there is danger near.

Its sharp nose sniffs the air and tells
If there are any dangerous smells.

Its sharp eyes peer from left to right
Watching for movements in the night.

If it senses it's safe, then up it leaps
And off across the fields it creeps.

John Foster

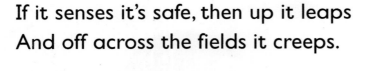

Grandad's beard

My grandad bends
To cuddle and kiss me.
But sometimes I wish
That he would miss me.

His beard always
Scrapes and scratches.
My cheek gets to feel
Like a box of matches.

John Kitching

Printed in Hong Kong